G R A D E
05
PIANO

**Pieces & Exercises for
Trinity College London
Exams 2018-2020**

Published by
Trinity College London Press
trinitycollege.com

Registered in England
Company no. 09726123

Copyright © 2017 Trinity College London Press
First impression, June 2017

Printed in England by Halstan & Co Ltd., Amersham, Bucks

Andante in A

Hob I:53/II

Joseph Haydn
(1732–1809)

(1) ♪♪♪♪

Do not play the repeats in the exam.

[Blank page to facilitate page turns]

Scherzando

Second movement from *Sonata no. 1 in G major*

Matthew Camidge
(1758-1844)

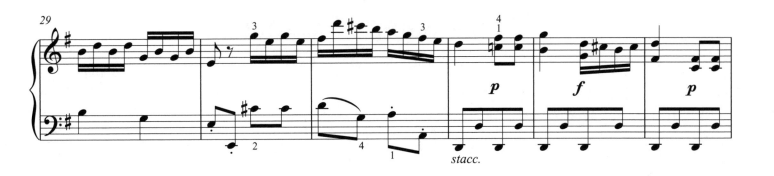

There Sleeps Titania

from *Midsummer Night*

William Alwyn
(1905-1985)

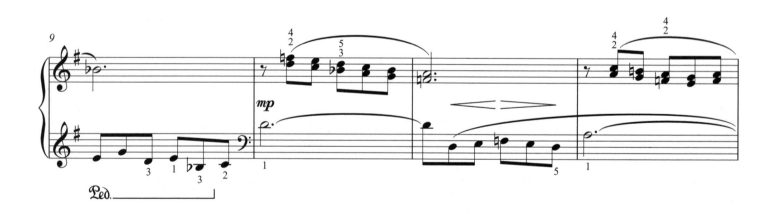

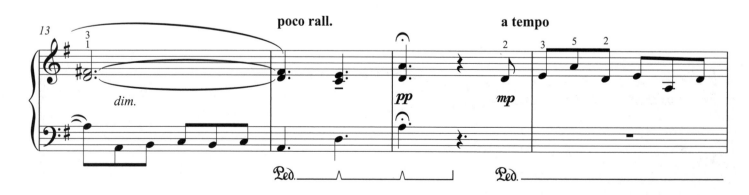

Taken from the *Midsummer Night* suite by William Alwyn. Reprinted by kind permission of the publisher

Andantino

First movement from *Sonatina no. 2*

Pál Járdányi
(1920-1966)

Blues for Beth

Mike Cornick
(b. 1947)

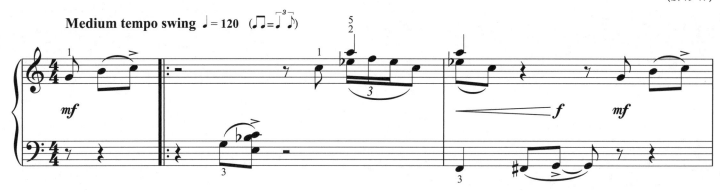

[Blank page to facilitate page turns]

Circus Theme

Fishel Pustilnik
(b. 1948)

Play the repeats in the exam.

And Now Let's Handel

Michael Proksch
(b. 1958)

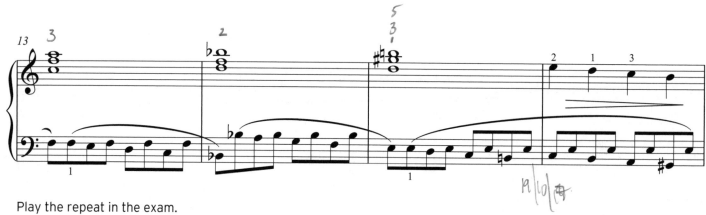

Play the repeat in the exam.

A Walk at Strumble Head

Gareth Balch
(b. 1969)

[Blank page to facilitate page turns]

All is Calm

Dennis Alexander
(b. 1947)

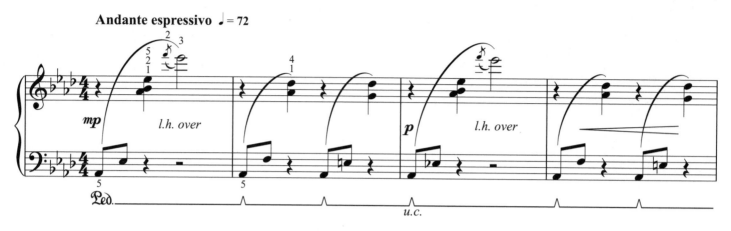

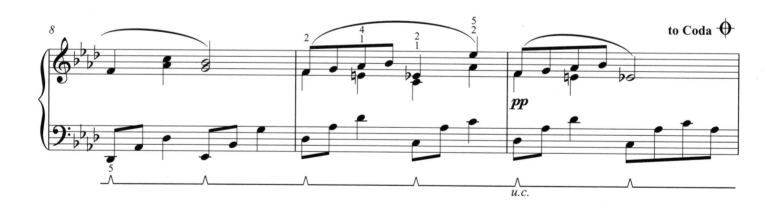

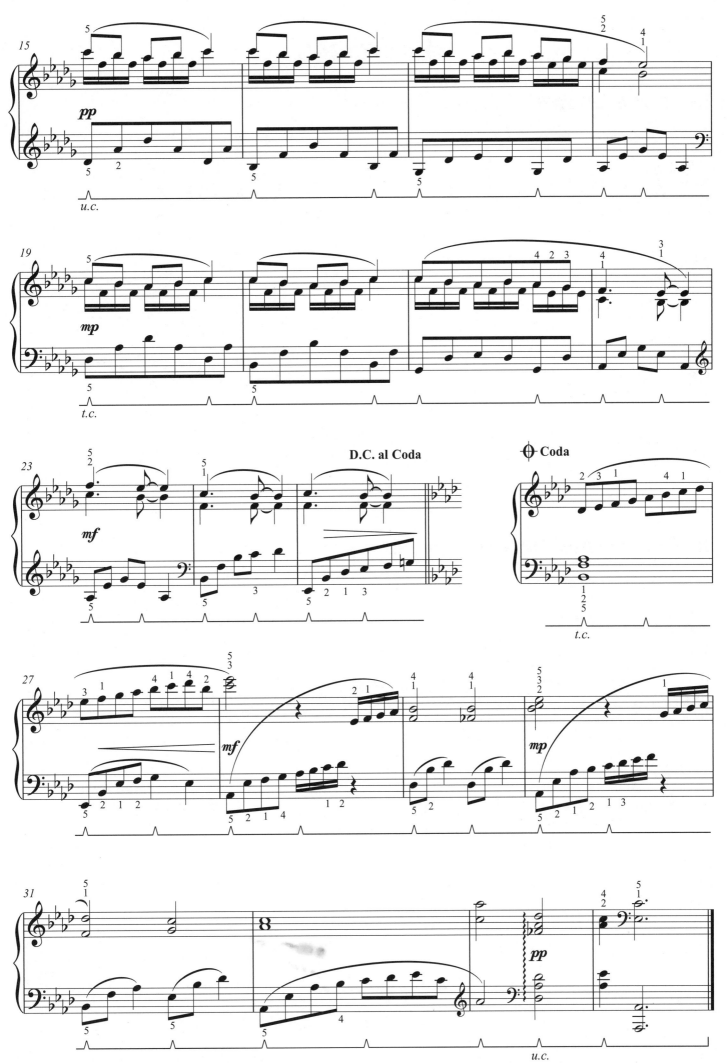

Exercises

1a. In the Chapel – tone, balance and voicing

1b. Ornamental Garden – tone, balance and voicing